Mum and Dad went to a car boot sale. They took the children.

Mum looked at a dinghy. She called
Dad. Dad looked at the dinghy.

"What is it?" asked Dad.
"It's a dinghy," said Mum.

Mum wanted the dinghy. She called
the children.
"Look at this," she said.

The children looked at the dinghy.
"What is it?" they asked.
"It's a dinghy," said Mum.

They took the dinghy home. Dad
pumped it up but it went down
again.

Mum mended the dinghy. She put a patch on it. The children helped.

Dad put the dinghy on the car. They took a picnic and went to the river.

Dad looked at the river. He pointed
at the weir.
"The weir is dangerous," he said.

Mum and Dad had a good idea.
"Let's put everything in the dinghy.
Everyone can help," they said.

They found a good spot for
the picnic. The children paddled
the dinghy.

It was time for the picnic. Mum
and Dad put the rug down and got
the picnic out.

Floppy ran out of the water. He
shook water over Dad.
"Go away, Floppy!" said Dad.

The river was busy. Biff and Chip
watched the boats go by.

Biff liked the big boats.
"I wish we could go on a big boat,"
she said.

It was time to go home.
"What a good day!" said Dad. "It
was a good picnic."

"Look!" said Biff. "There is nobody on that boat."

"My boat is in danger," called a
lady. "Help! Get my boat!"

Mum put the dinghy in the river. She
paddled to the boat.
"Be careful," called everyone.

Mum climbed on to the boat. She
started the engine. She was just
in time.

Mum brought the boat back.
"Hooray!" everyone shouted.
"Mum to the rescue!" said Kipper.

Dad let go of the dinghy rope. The
dinghy went over the weir.
"Oh no!" said everyone.

The lady had an idea.
"I will lend you my boat to say
thank you," she said.

The family had a holiday on the boat.
"Thanks to the dinghy," said Mum.